THE GOLDEN
SONG BOOK

Selected and arranged by
KATHARINE TYLER WESSELLS

Illustrated by
GERTRUDE ELLIOTT

 GOLDEN PRESS • NEW YORK
Western Publishing Company, Inc.
Racine, Wisconsin

DEDICATED TO KATHLEEN

Acknowledgment

The compiler and the publishers acknowledge
with gratitude the invaluable assistance of
Kurt Stone in the preparation of this book.

Twenty-Eighth Printing, 1976

GOLDEN, A GOLDEN BOOK® and GOLDEN PRESS® are trademarks of
Western Publishing Company, Inc.

Library of Congress Catalog Card Number: 65-7398

CONTENTS

*Suggestions for singing games have been included
for some songs. These are indicated by asterisks.*

ADESTE FIDELES 50

AU CLAIR DE LA LUNE 57

AWAY IN A MANGER 49

BAA, BAA, BLACK SHEEP 24

BILLY BOY 52

BYE, BABY HUNTING 58

CRADLE SONG 60

*DID YOU EVER SEE A LASSIE? 36

*FARMER IN THE DELL, THE 9

FRÈRE JACQUES 21

FROG HE WOULD A-WOOING GO, A 28

HEY DIDDLE DIDDLE 32

HICKORY, DICKORY, DOCK 10

HUMPTY DUMPTY 47

HUSH, MY BABE 62

I HAD A LITTLE NUT TREE 54

I LOVE LITTLE PUSSY 15

JACK AND JILL 24

JACK HORNER 16

JESUS LOVES ME 61

JESUS, TENDER SHEPHERD 63

JINGLE BELLS 64

JOLLY MILLER, THE 26

LITTLE BOY BLUE 23

*LONDON BRIDGE 43

*LOOBY-LOO 46

MARY HAD A LITTLE LAMB 11

MISTRESS MARY, QUITE CONTRARY 16

*MUFFIN MAN, THE 53

*OATS, PEAS, BEANS, AND BARLEY GROW 27

OH, DEAR! WHAT CAN THE MATTER BE? 44

OH SUSANNA 38

OLD KING COLE 34

OLD MacDONALD HAD A FARM 12

*OPEN THE GATES AS HIGH AS THE SKY 31

*PETITES MARIONETTES, LES 55

POLLY PUT THE KETTLE ON 59

POP! GOES THE WEASEL 33

RIDE A COCK-HORSE 37

RIG A JIG JIG 41

RING AROUND A ROSY 31

ROCKABYE, BABY 56

*ROUND THE MULBERRY BUSH 17

*ROUND THE VILLAGE 25

ROW, ROW, ROW YOUR BOAT 10

SCOTLAND'S BURNING 35

SEE-SAW 14

SHE'LL BE COMIN' 'ROUND THE MOUNTAIN 30

SILENT NIGHT 48

SING A SONG OF SIXPENCE 22

STAR-SPANGLED BANNER, THE 67

THREE BLIND MICE 66

THREE LITTLE KITTENS 18

*TISKET, A TASKET, A 20

TWINKLE, TWINKLE, LITTLE STAR 69

YANKEE DOODLE 40

The farmer in the dell,
The farmer in the dell,

The farmer takes a wife

The child takes a nurse

Heigh-o, the derry-o, the farmer in the dell.

THE FARMER IN THE DELL

GAME: Children form a ring with one child as "farmer" in the middle. They join hands and sing while marching around the farmer. The "farmer" chooses a "wife," etc. Finally the "cheese" is clapped out and must begin again as farmer.

Old singing game   Harmonized by Katharine Tyler Wessells   Words and tune traditional

The farm-er in the dell, The farm-er in the dell, Heigh-o, the

der - ry- o, The farm - er in the dell.

The dog takes a cat,
The dog takes a cat,
Heigh-o, the derry-o,
The dog takes a cat.

The cat takes a rat,
The cat takes a rat,
Heigh-o, the derry-o,
The cat takes a rat.

The farmer takes a wife,
The farmer takes a wife,
Heigh-ho, the derry-o,
The farmer takes a wife.

The wife takes a child,
The wife takes a child,
Heigh-o, the derry-o,
The wife takes a child.

The child takes a nurse,
The child takes a nurse,
Heigh-o, the derry-o,
The child takes a nurse.

The nurse takes a dog,
The nurse takes a dog,
Heigh-o, the derry-o,
The nurse takes a dog.

The rat takes a cheese,
The rat takes a cheese,
Heigh-o, the derry-o,
The rat takes a cheese.

The cheese stands alone!
The cheese stands alone!
Heigh-o, the derry-o,
The cheese stands alone!

9

ROW, ROW, ROW YOUR BOAT

Old round   Harmonized by Katharine Tyler Wessells   Words and tune traditional

Row, row, row your boat, Gent - ly down the stream,

Mer- ri - ly, mer- ri - ly, mer- ri - ly, mer- ri - ly, Life is but a dream.

HICKORY, DICKORY, DOCK

Words from Mother Goose   Harmonized by Katharine Tyler Wessells   Tune traditional

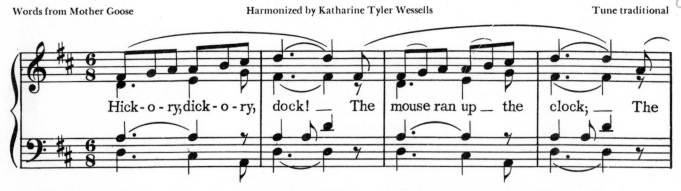

Hick- o - ry, dick - o - ry, dock! — The mouse ran up — the clock; — The

clock struck one, The mouse ran down, Hick- o - ry, dick - o - ry, dock! —

MARY HAD A LITTLE LAMB

Words and tune traditional

Harmonized by Katharine Tyler Wessells

Ma - ry had a lit - tle lamb, lit - tle lamb, lit - tle lamb,

Ma - ry had a lit - tle lamb, Its fleece was white as snow.

And everywhere that Mary went,
Mary went, Mary went,
Everywhere that Mary went,
The lamb was sure to go.

It followed her to school one day,
School one day, school one day,
Followed her to school one day,
Which was against the rule.

It made the children laugh and play,
Laugh and play, laugh and play,
Made the children laugh and play,
To see a lamb at school.

OLD MACDONALD HAD A FARM

Words and tune traditional

Harmonized by Katharine Tyler Wessells

Old Mac-Don-ald had a farm, Ee-igh, ee-igh, oh! And on this farm he had some chicks, Ee-igh, ee-igh, oh! With a chick, chick here and a chick, chick there; Here a chick, there a chick, Every-where a chick, chick. Old Mac-Don-ald had a farm, Ee-igh, ee-igh, oh!

Old MacDonald had a farm, Ee-igh, ee-igh, oh!
And on this farm he had some ducks, Ee-igh, ee-igh, oh!
With a quack, quack here, and a quack, quack there;
Here a quack, there a quack, everywhere a quack, quack,
With a chick, chick here, and a chick, chick there,
Here a chick, there a chick, everywhere a chick, chick.
Old MacDonald had a farm, Ee-igh, ee-igh, oh!

Old MacDonald had a farm, Ee-igh, ee-igh, oh!
And on this farm he had some turkeys, Ee-igh, ee-igh, oh!
With a gobble, gobble here, and a gobble, gobble there;
Here a gobble, there a gobble, everywhere a gobble, gobble,
With a quack, quack here, and a quack, quack there;
Here a quack, there a quack, everywhere a quack, quack,
With a chick, chick here, and a chick, chick there;
Here a chick, there a chick, everywhere a chick, chick.
Old MacDonald had a farm, Ee-igh, ee-igh, oh!

Old MacDonald had a farm, Ee-igh, ee-igh, oh!
And on this farm he had some pigs, Ee-igh, ee-igh, oh!
With an oink, oink here, and an oink, oink there;
Here an oink, there an oink, everywhere an oink, oink,
With a gobble, gobble here, and a gobble, gobble there;
Here a gobble, there a gobble, everywhere a gobble, gobble,
With a quack, quack here, and a quack, quack there;
Here a quack, there a quack, everywhere a quack, quack,
With a chick, chick here, and a chick, chick there;
Here a chick, there a chick, everywhere a chick, chick.
Old MacDonald had a farm, Ee-igh, ee-igh, oh!

Old MacDonald had a farm, Ee-igh, ee-igh, oh!
And on this farm he had some cows, Ee-igh, ee-igh, oh!
With a moo, moo here, etc.

Old MacDonald had a farm, Ee-igh, ee-igh, oh!
And on this farm he had some donkeys, Ee-igh, ee-igh, oh!
With a hee, haw here, etc.

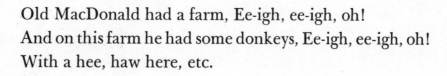

SEE-SAW

Words from Mother Goose   Harmonized by Katharine Tyler Wessells   Melody by J. W. Elliott

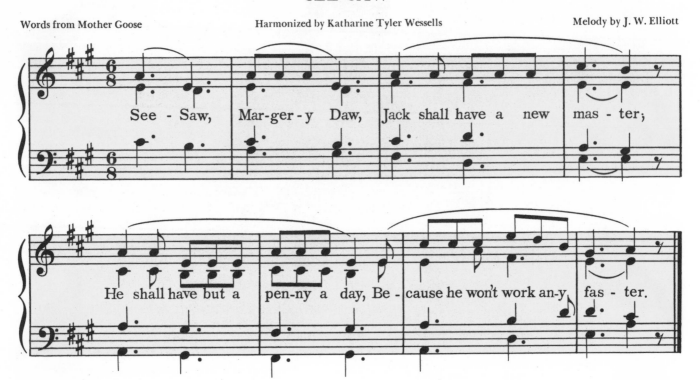

See - Saw, Mar-ger-y Daw, Jack shall have a new mas - ter;

He shall have but a pen-ny a day, Be - cause he won't work an-y fas - ter.

I LOVE LITTLE PUSSY

Words from Mother Goose   Harmonized by Katharine Tyler Wessells   Melody by J. W. Elliott

I — love lit-tle pus-sy, Her coat is so warm, And— if I don't hurt her, She'll do me no harm; I'll— sit by the fire— and give her some food, And— pus-sy will love me be-cause I am good.

15

JACK HORNER

Words from Mother Goose   Harmonized by Katharine Tyler Wessells   Melody by J. W. Elliott

Lit-tle Jack Horn-er sat in a corn-er, Eat-ing a Christ-mas pie; ___ He

put in his thumb and pulled out a plum, And said, "What a good boy am I!" ___

MISTRESS MARY, QUITE CONTRARY

Words from Mother Goose   Harmonized by Katharine Tyler Wessells   Tune traditional

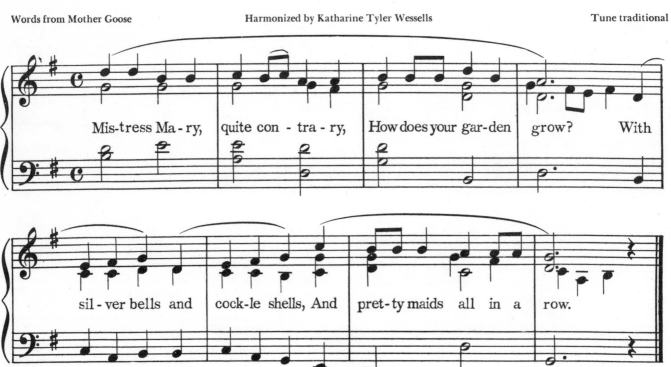

Mis-tress Ma-ry, quite con-tra-ry, How does your gar-den grow? With

sil-ver bells and cock-le shells, And pret-ty maids all in a row.

16

'ROUND THE MULBERRY BUSH

GAME: Suit the actions to the words.

Singing game

Harmonized by Katharine Tyler Wessells

Words and tune traditional

Here we go round the mul-ber-ry bush, The mul-ber-ry bush, the mul-ber-ry bush;

Here we go round the mul-ber-ry bush, So ear-ly in the morn-ing.

This is the way we wash our clothes,
We wash our clothes, we wash our clothes;
This is the way we wash our clothes,
So early Monday morning.

This is the way we iron our clothes,
We iron our clothes, we iron our clothes;
This is the way we iron our clothes,
So early Tuesday morning.

This is the way we scrub the floor,
We scrub the floor, we scrub the floor;
This is the way we scrub the floor,
So early Wednesday morning.

This is the way we mend our clothes,
We mend our clothes, we mend our clothes;
This is the way we mend our clothes,
So early Thursday morning.

This is the way we sweep the house,
We sweep the house, we sweep the house;
This is the way we sweep the house,
So early Friday morning.

This is the way we bake our bread,
We bake our bread, we bake our bread;
This is the way we bake our bread,
So early Saturday morning.

This is the way we go to church,
We go to church, we go to church;
This is the way we go to church,
So early Sunday morning.

THREE LITTLE KITTENS

Words from Mother Goose   Harmonized by Katharine Tyler Wessells   Tune traditional

The three lit-tle kit-tens, they lost their mit-tens, And they be-gan to cry, ___ "Oh,

Mam - my dear, we sad - ly fear Our mit - tens we have lost!" ___ "What!

lost your mit-tens, you naugh - ty kit-tens? Then you shall have no pie!"

The three little kittens, they found their mittens,
And they began to cry,
"Oh, Mammy dear, see here, see here,
Our mittens we have found."
"What! found your mittens, you good little kittens?
Then you shall have some pie."
"Purr, purr, purr, purr,
We shall have some pie."

The three little kittens put on their mittens
And soon ate up the pie.
"Oh, Mammy dear, we greatly fear
Our mittens we have soiled."
"What! soiled your mittens, you naughty kittens?"
Then they began to sigh,
"Mi-ew, mi-ew,"
They began to sigh.

The three little kittens, they washed their mittens,
And hung them up to dry.
"Oh, Mammy dear, look here, look here,
Our mittens we have washed."
"What! washed your mittens, you darling kittens?
But I smell a rat close by!
Hush! hush! hush! hush!
I smell a rat close by!"

A TISKET, A TASKET

GAME: This is a "drop-the-handkerchief" game. Children, holding each other's hands, stand in a circle. The child who is "it," carrying the handkerchief, runs around the outside, while they all sing. He drops the handkerchief when he comes to the person of his choice, and then continues running around the circle. The other child runs in the opposite direction, and each tries to reach the vacant place first. The one who is last takes the handkerchief for the next round.

Old singing game   Harmonized by Katharine Tyler Wessells   Words and tune traditional

A tis-ket, a tas-ket, A green and yel-low bas-ket, I wrote a let-ter to my love, And on the way I dropped it, I dropped it, I dropped it, And on the way I dropped it. A lit-tle {boy / girl} picked it up And put it in {his / her} pock-et.

FRÈRE JACQUES

Old French round

Harmonized by Katharine Tyler Wessells

Words, tune, and translation traditional

Frè-re Jacques, Frè-re Jacques, Dor-mez vous? Dor-mez vous? Son-nez les ma-
Are you sleeping? Are you sleeping, Brother John, Broth-er John? Morning bells are

ti - nes, Son-nez les ma- ti - nes: Din, Din, Don, Din, Din, Don.
ring-ing, Morning bells are ring-ing: Ding, Ding, Dong, Ding, Ding, Dong.

21

SING A SONG OF SIXPENCE

Words from Mother Goose Harmonized by Katharine Tyler Wessells Melody by J. W. Elliott

Sing a song of six-pence, A pock-et full of rye, Four and twen-ty black-birds

baked in a pie; When the pie was o-pened, The birds be-gan to sing;

Was-n't that a dain-ty dish to set be-fore a king? The

king was in his counting house, Counting out his mon-ey, The queen was in the par-lor,

Eat - ing bread and hon - ey, The maid was in the gar - den,

Hang-ing out the clothes, There came a lit - tle black-bird and pecked off her nose.

LITTLE BOY BLUE

Words from Mother Goose

Harmonized by Katharine Tyler Wessells

Tune traditional

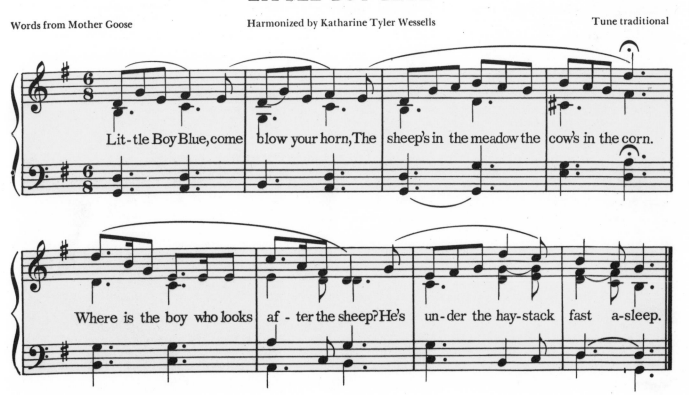

Lit - tle Boy Blue, come blow your horn, The sheep's in the meadow the cow's in the corn.

Where is the boy who looks af - ter the sheep? He's un-der the hay-stack fast a-sleep.

BAA, BAA, BLACK SHEEP

Words from Mother Goose — Harmonized by Katharine Tyler Wessells — Tune traditional

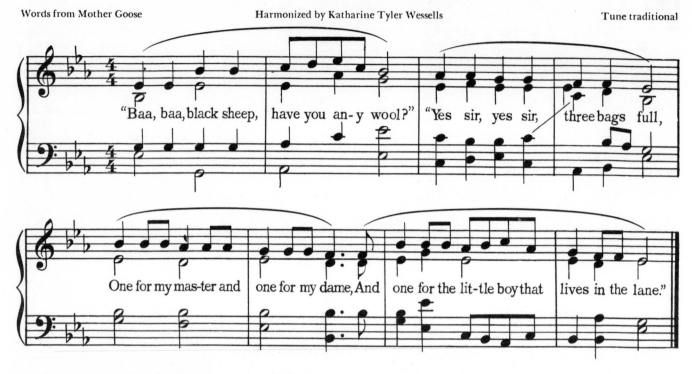

"Baa, baa, black sheep, have you an-y wool?" "Yes sir, yes sir, three bags full,

One for my mas-ter and one for my dame, And one for the lit-tle boy that lives in the lane."

JACK AND JILL

Words from Mother Goose — Harmonized by Katharine Tyler Wessells — Melody by J. W. Elliott

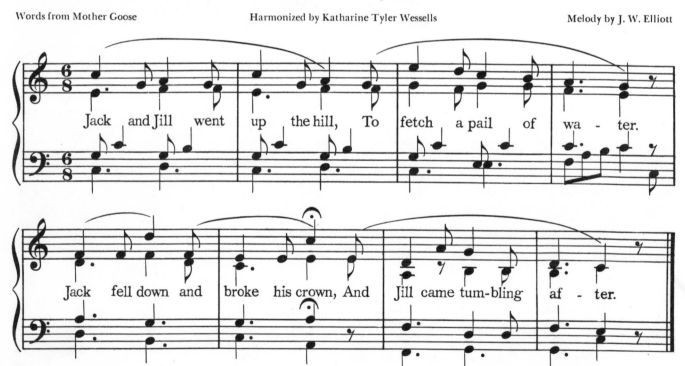

Jack and Jill went up the hill, To fetch a pail of wa - ter.

Jack fell down and broke his crown, And Jill came tum-bling af - ter.

Then up Jack got, and home did trot,
As fast as he could caper.
He went to bed and plastered his head
With vinegar and brown paper.

Jill came in and she did grin,
To see his paper plaster.
Mother, vexed, did whip her next,
For causing Jack's disaster.

24

ROUND THE VILLAGE

GAME: Children stand in a circle and pretend they are houses in a village. One child is "it" and runs round and round the village during the first verse. At the second verse the children join hands and raise their arms high to make windows, while the child runs in and out. During the third verse, the child looks around the circle, pauses, and then chooses a partner. At the fourth verse ("Follow me to London") the first child leads his partner around the circle; but they return at the end of the verse to the center of the circle, where they shake hands, bow, and part (fifth verse). The first child then takes his place in the circle and the second is "it."

Old singing game   Harmonized by Katharine Tyler Wessells   Words and tune traditional

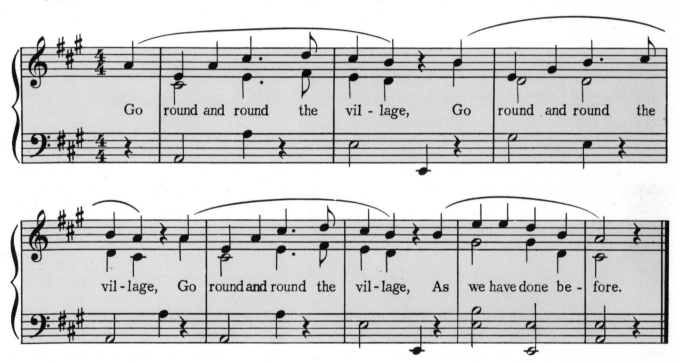

Go round and round the vil-lage, Go round and round the vil-lage, Go round and round the vil-lage, As we have done be-fore.

Go in and out the windows,
Go in and out the windows,
Go in and out the windows,
As we have done before.

Now stand and face your partner,
Now stand and face your partner,
Now stand and face your partner,
And bow before you go.

Now follow me to London,
Now follow me to London,
Now follow me to London,
As we have done before.

Now shake his hand and leave him,
Now shake his hand and leave him,
Now shake his hand and leave him,
And bow before you go.

25

THE JOLLY MILLER

Words and tune traditional

Harmonized by Katharine Tyler Wessells

There was a jol - ly mil - ler once Lived on the Riv - er Dee. He

worked and sang from morn till night, No lark more blithe than he. And

this the bur - den of his song For - ev - er used to be: "I

care for no-bod-y, no not I, If no-bod-y cares for me."

OATS, PEAS, BEANS, AND BARLEY GROW

GAME: Children, singing, circle around a child in the middle (the farmer), suiting gestures to words. At the third verse the farmer chooses a partner, and at the fourth verse they both kneel and salute.

Old singing game   Harmonized by Katharine Tyler Wessells   Tune traditional (French)

Oats, peas, beans, and bar - ley grows, Oats, peas, beans, and bar - ley grows, Nor you nor I nor an - y - one knows How oats, peas, beans, and bar - ley grows.

Thus the farmer sows his seed,
Stands erect and takes his ease,
He stamps his foot and claps his hands,
And turns around to view his lands.

Waiting for a partner,
Waiting for a partner,
Open the ring and take her in,
While we all gaily dance and sing.

Now you're married you must obey,
You must be true to all you say,
You must be kind, you must be good,
And make your husband chop the wood!

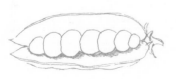

27

A FROG, HE WOULD A-WOOING GO

Words and tune from Ednah P. C. Hayes

Harmonized by Katharine Tyler Wessells

A frog, he would a-woo-ing go, Hm-m, hm-m,

Frog he would a-woo-ing go, And he dressed himself from top to toe, Hm-m, hm-m.

28

"Uncle Rat, is Miss Mouse within?
Hm-m, hm-m-m,
Uncle Rat, is Miss Mouse within?"
"Yes, in the parlor, learning to spin,
Hm-m, hm-m-m."

"Oh, Miss Mouse, will you marry me?
Hm-m, hm-m-m,
Oh, Miss Mouse, will you marry me?"
"Yes, if Uncle Rat will agree,
Hm-m, hm-m-m."

"Uncle Rat has gone to town.
Hm-m, hm-m-m,
Uncle Rat has gone to town,
To buy Miss Mouse a wedding gown,
Hm-m, hm-m-m."

"Where shall the wedding supper be?
Hm-m, hm-m-m,
Where shall the wedding supper be?"
"Way down yonder in the hollow tree,
Hm-m, hm-m-m."

First came in was the old tom-cat,
Hm-m, hm-m-m,
First came in was the old tom-cat,
And he danced a jig with Mistress Rat,
Hm-m, hm-m-m.

Next came in was the bumble-bee,
Hm-m, hm-m-m,
Next came in was the bumble-bee,
And he danced a jig with old Miss Flea,
Hm-m, hm-m-m.

"And what do you think they had for supper?
Hm-m, hm-m-m,
And what do you think they had for supper?"
"Black-eyed peas, corn pone, and butter,
Hm-m, hm-m-m."

"And what do you think they had to drink?
Hm-m, hm-m-m,
And what do you think they had to drink?"
"Persimmon beer and a bottle of ink,
Hm-m, hm-m-m."

And after supper the old tom-cat,
Hm-m, hm-m-m,
And after supper the old tom-cat,
He ate up the frog, the mouse, and the rat,
Hm-m, hm-m-m.

Saddle and bridle on the shelf,
Hm-m, hm-m-m,
Saddle and bridle on the shelf,
If you want any more you can sing it yourself,
Hm-m, hm-m-m.

SHE'LL BE COMIN' 'ROUND THE MOUNTAIN

Old American chanty   Harmonized by Katharine Tyler Wessells   Words and music traditional

She'll be drivin' six white horses when she comes, etc.

We will all be out to meet her when she comes, etc.

We will kill the old red rooster when she comes, etc.

OPEN THE GATES AS HIGH AS THE SKY

GAME: Two children join hands, forming an arch ("gates"), first agreeing between themselves which of them represents a diamond necklace and which a pearl pin. The others, in line, pass under and try to get safely by, before the gates fall on the head of an unfortunate one, who is made to choose which he will have, a diamond necklace or a pearl pin. He then gets behind the gate which represents his choice, and after all are caught there is a tug of war.

Singing game   Harmonized by Katharine Tyler Wessells   Words and tune traditional

In stately rhythm

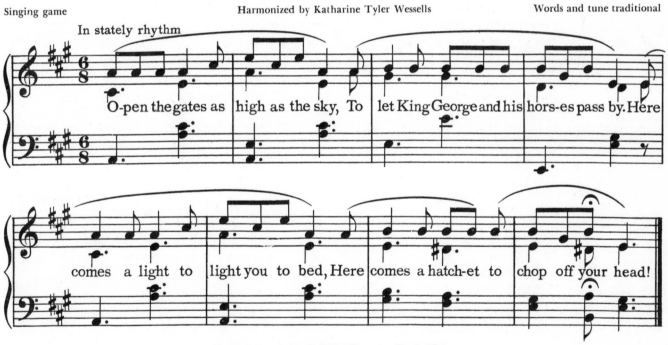

O-pen the gates as high as the sky, To let King George and his hors-es pass by. Here

comes a light to light you to bed, Here comes a hatch-et to chop off your head!

RING AROUND A ROSY

Old singing game   Harmonized by Katharine Tyler Wessells   Words and tune traditional

Ring a-round a ros-y, A pock-et full of po-sies, Ash-es, Ash-es, We all fall down!

31

HEY DIDDLE DIDDLE

Words from Mother Goose   Harmonized by Katharine Tyler Wessells   Tune traditional

Hey, did-dle, did-dle, the cat and the fid-dle, The cow jumped o-ver the moon;-- The lit-tle dog laughed to see such sport, And the dish ran a-way with the spoon, spoon, spoon, The dish ran a-way with the spoon.

POP! GOES THE WEASEL

Words and tune traditional

Harmonized by Katharine Tyler Wessells

All a-round the cob-bler's bench, The mon-key chased the wea-sel, The mon-key thought 'twas all in fun, Pop! goes the wea-sel. A pen-ny for a spool of thread, A pen-ny for a nee-dle, That's the way the mon-ey goes, Pop! goes the wea-sel.

OLD KING COLE

Words from Mother Goose   Harmonized by Katharine Tyler Wessells   Tune traditional

Old King Cole was a mer-ry old__ soul, And a mer-ry old soul was he;____ He__ called for his pipe and he called for his bowl, And he called for his fid-dlers__ three. Ev'-ry__ fid-dler__

34

had a fine _ fid-dle And a ver-y fine _ fid-dle had he, _____ Tweedle

dum, Tweedle dee went the fid-dlers three, Tweedle dum, dee, dum, dee, deedle dee!

SCOTLAND'S BURNING

Old round   Harmonized by Katharine Tyler Wessells   Words and tune traditional

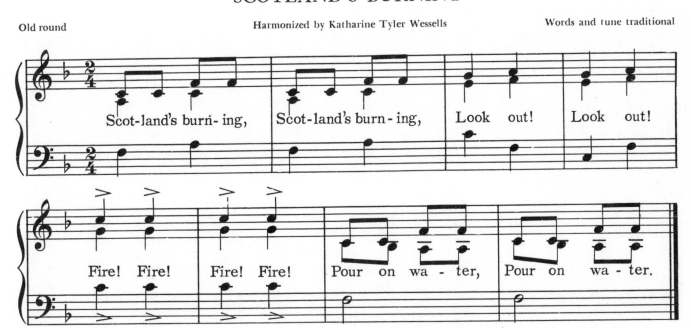

Scot-land's burn-ing, Scot-land's burn-ing, Look out! Look out!

Fire! Fire! Fire! Fire! Pour on wa-ter, Pour on wa-ter.

DID YOU EVER SEE A LASSIE?

GAME: Form a single circle, hands joined, with one child in center. Measures 1-8: Skip around to the left during the first two lines of song. As words "do this way and that" are sung, the child in the center imitates some activity. Measures 9-16: All drop hands, face center of circle, and imitate leader.

Old singing game   Harmonized by Katharine Tyler Wessells   Words and tune traditional

Did you ev - er see a { las - sie, a / lad-die, a } las - sie, a / lad - die, a las - sie? / lad-die? Did you ev - er see a { las - sie / lad - die go this way and that? Go this way and that way and this way and that way? Did you

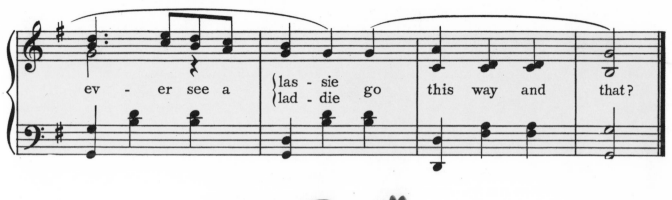

ev - er see a las - sie / lad - die go this way and that?

RIDE A COCK-HORSE

Words from Mother Goose   Harmonized by Katharine Tyler Wessells   Melody by J. W. Elliott

Ride a cock-horse, to Ban-bur-y Cross, To see a fine la-dy up-

on a white horse; Rings on her fin-gers, and bells on her toes,

She shall have mu-sic wher-ev-er she goes.

OH SUSANNA

Words and music by Stephen Foster

Transposed by Katharine Tyler Wessells

I __ came to Al - a - ba-ma wid my ban-jo on my knee, I'm __

goin' to Lou-si - an-a, My __ true love for to see. It __

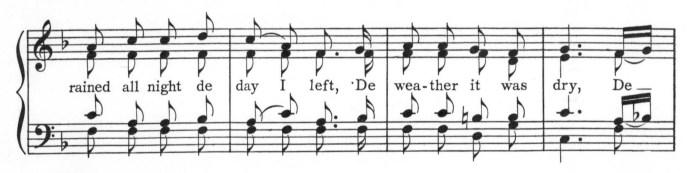

rained all night de day I left, 'De wea-ther it was dry, De __

I had a dream de odder night, when eb'rything
　　was still;
I thought I saw Susanna, a-coming down de hill.
De buckwheat cake was in her mouth, de tear
　　was in her eye,
Says I, "I'm coming from de South, Susanna don't
　　you cry."
Oh Susanna, oh don't you cry for me,
For I'm goin' to Lou'siana wid' my banjo on
　　my knee.

38

sun so hot I froze to death, Su - san - na, don't you cry!

Oh Su - san - na, oh don't you cry for me, For I'm

goin' to Lou - si - an - a wid my ban - jo on my knee.

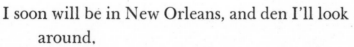

I soon will be in New Orleans, and den I'll look
    around,
And when I find Susanna, I'll fall upon de ground,
But if I do not find her, dis darkie'll surely
    die,
And when I'm dead and buried, Susanna don't
    you cry.
Oh Susanna, oh don't you cry for me,
For I'm goin' to Lou'siana wid' my banjo on my
    knee.

YANKEE DOODLE

Words and tune traditional

Harmonized by Katharine Tyler Wessells

Yan-kee Doo-dle went to town up - on a lit - tle po - ny, He

stuck a feath-er in his cap and called it mac-a - ro - ni.

Yan - kee Doo-dle, Doo-dle Doo, Yan - kee Doo-dle Dan-dy,

40

All the las - sies are so smart and sweet as sug - ar can - dy.

Fath'r and I went down to camp,
Along with Captain Goodin,
And there we saw the men and boys,
As thick as hasty puddin'.
Yankee Doodle keep it up, Yankee Doodle dandy,
Mind the music and the step, and with the girls
    be handy.

RIG A JIG JIG

Old American chanty

Harmonized by Katharine Tyler Wessells

As I was walk-ing down the street, Heigh-o! Heigh-o! Heigh-o! Heigh-o! A

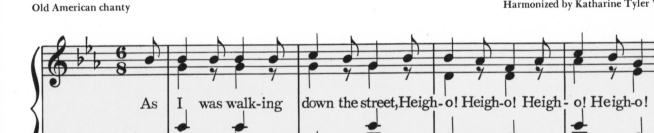

pret - ty girl __ I chanced to meet, Heigh - o! Heigh-o - o! Heigh - o!. __

Rig - a - jig-jig and a - way we go, a - way we go, a - way we go,

Rig - a - jig-jig and a - way we go, Heigh - o! Heigh-o - o! Heigh - o! ___ Heigh-

o! Heigh-o! Heigh - o! Heigh-o! Heigh - o! Heigh-o! Heigh - o! Heigh-o!

Rig- a - jig-jig and a - way we go, Heigh - o! Heigh-o - o! Heigh - o! ___

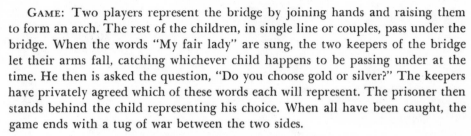

LONDON BRIDGE

GAME: Two players represent the bridge by joining hands and raising them to form an arch. The rest of the children, in single line or couples, pass under the bridge. When the words "My fair lady" are sung, the two keepers of the bridge let their arms fall, catching whichever child happens to be passing under at the time. He then is asked the question, "Do you choose gold or silver?" The keepers have privately agreed which of these words each will represent. The prisoner then stands behind the child representing his choice. When all have been caught, the game ends with a tug of war between the two sides.

Singing game   Harmonized by Katharine Tyler Wessells   Words and tune traditional

Lon - don Bridge is fall - ing down, Fall - ing down, fall - ing down,

Lon - don Bridge is fall - ing down, My fair la - dy!

Build it up with iron bars, etc.

Iron bars will bend and break, etc.

Build it up with pins and needles, etc.

Pins and needles rust and bend, etc.

Build it up with penny loaves, etc.

Penny loaves will tumble down, etc.

Build it up with gold and silver, etc.

Gold and silver I've not got, etc.

Here's a prisoner I have got, etc.

What's the prisoner done to you, etc.

Stole my watch and broke my chain, etc.

What'll you take to set him free, etc.

One hundred pounds will set him free, etc.

One hundred pounds we have not got, etc.

Then off to prison he must go, etc.

43

OH, DEAR! WHAT CAN THE MATTER BE?

Words and tune traditional

Harmonized by Katharine Tyler Wessells

Oh, dear! What can the mat-ter be? Dear, dear! What can the mat-ter be?

Oh, dear! What can the mat-ter be? John-ny's so long at the fair. He

promised he'd buy me a fairing should please me, And then for a kiss, Oh, he vowed he would tease me, He

promised he'd buy me a bunch of blue ribbons, To tie up my bonnie brown hair. ___

Oh, dear! What can the mat-ter be? Dear, dear! What can the mat-ter be?

Oh, dear! What can the mat-ter be? John-ny's so long at the fair.

Oh, dear! What can the matter be?
Dear, dear! What can the matter be?
Oh, dear! What can the matter be?
Johnny's so long at the fair.
He promised he'd bring me a basket of posies,
A garland of lilies, a garland of roses,

A little straw hat to set off the blue ribbons
That tie up my bonnie brown hair.
Oh, dear! What can the matter be?
Dear, dear! What can the matter be?
Oh, dear! What can the matter be?
Johnny's so long at the fair.

LOOBY-LOO

GAME: Form a single circle, hands joined. Skip to left until words "Saturday night" are sung. All put right hands in toward the center of the circle, then stretch right hands away from the center of the circle. All shake right hands hard and turn in place. Repeat for. following verses, suiting action to words.

Old singing game

Words and tune traditional

Here we dance Loo-by - loo, Here we dance Loo-by - light,

Here we dance Loo-by - loo, All on a Sat-ur-day night.__ I

put my right hand in, __ I put my right hand out, __ I

give my right hand a shake, shake, shake, And turn my-self a - bout.

I put my left hand in, etc.   I put my right foot in, etc.   I put my left foot in, etc.

I put my little head in, etc.   I put my whole self in, etc.

HUMPTY DUMPTY

Words from Mother Goose

Tune and arrangement by J. W. Elliott

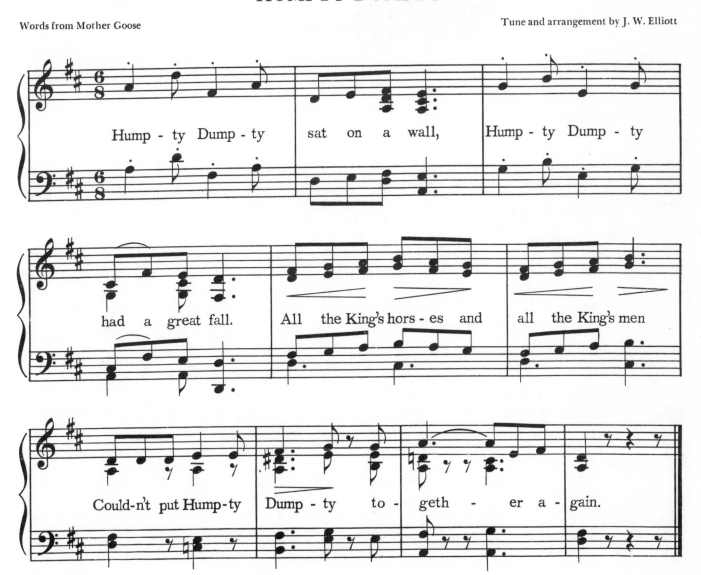

Humpty Dumpty sat on a wall, Humpty Dumpty had a great fall. All the King's horses and all the King's men Couldn't put Humpty Dumpty together again.

SILENT NIGHT

Words by Joseph Mohr   Arranged by Katharine Tyler Wessells   Music by Franz Gruber

Schlaf in himm-li-scher Ruh,____ Schlaf___ in himm-li-scher Ruh!
Sleep in heav-en-ly peace,____ Sleep___ in heav-en-ly peace.

AWAY IN A MANGER

Words by Martin Luther   Harmonized by Katharine Tyler Wessells   Old German tune

A - way in a man-ger, no crib for a bed, The lit - tle Lord

Je - sus laid down His sweet head; The stars in the sky ___ looked

down where He lay, The lit - tle Lord Je - sus, a - sleep on the hay.

ADESTE FIDELES

Translated by F. Oakley

Melody by John Reading

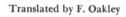

Ad - es - te fi - de - les, lae - ti tri - um - phan - tes; Ve -
O come, all ye faith - ful, Joy - ful and tri - um - phant, O

ni - te, ve - ni - te, in Beth - le - hem.
come ye, O come ye to Beth - le - hem.

Na - tum vi - de - te, Re - gem an - ge - lo - rum; Ve -
Come and be - hold Him, *Born the King of* *an - gels, O*

ni - te a - do - re - mus, Ve - ni - te a - do - re - mus, Ve -
come, let us a - dore Him, O *come, let us a - dore Him, O*

ni - te a - do - re - mus __ Do - mi - num.
come, let us a - dore Him, __ Christ __ the Lord.

BILLY BOY

Words and tune traditional

Harmonized by Katharine Tyler Wessells

Oh, — where have you been, Bil - ly Boy, Bil - ly Boy, Oh, —

where have you been, charming Bil-ly? — I have been to seek a wife, She's the

joy — of my life, She's a young thing and can-not leave her moth-er. —

Did she bid you to come in, Billy Boy, Billy Boy? Yes, she bade me to come in,
Did she bid you to come in, charming Billy? There's a dimple in her chin,
She's a young thing and cannot leave her mother.

Did she set for you a chair, Billy Boy, Billy Boy? Yes, she set for me a chair,
Did she set for you a chair, charming Billy? She has ringlets in her hair,
She's a young thing and cannot leave her mother.

Can she make a cherry pie, Billy Boy, Billy Boy? She can make a cherry pie,
Can she make a cherry pie, charming Billy? Quick's a cat can wink her eye,
She's a young thing and cannot leave her mother.

THE MUFFIN MAN

GAME: Form one large circle with hands joined, skipping to the left. A child stands in the center and chooses a partner from the big circle by skipping toward the chosen one and offering both hands on the words, "Oh, yes we've seen the Muffin Man." The two occupying the center now join both hands and sing "Two have seen the Muffin Man" to the end of this verse. At the beginning of the next verse, these two choose partners from the ring, and the four join hands, singing, "Four have seen the Muffin Man." This is repeated until all are chosen and the big circle sings, "All have seen the Muffin Man." The two circles move in contrary directions.

Old singing game   Harmonized by Katharine Tyler Wessells   Words and tune traditional

Oh, do you know the Muf-fin Man, The Muf-fin Man, the Muf-fin Man, Oh, do you know the Muf-fin Man, That lives in Dru-ry Lane? Oh!

Oh, yes we've seen the Muffin Man,
The Muffin Man, the Muffin Man;
Oh, yes we've seen the Muffin Man,
That lives in Drury Lane! Oh!

53

I HAD A LITTLE NUT TREE

Words from Mother Goose

Harmonized by Katharine Tyler Wessells

Tune traditional

I had a lit-tle nut tree; noth-ing would it bear,

But a sil-ver nut-meg and a gold-en pear. The King of Spain's daugh-ter

came to vis-it me, And all — for the sake of my lit-tle nut tree.

LES PETITES MARIONETTES

GAME: Hold up both hands with the fingers stretched out like an open fan. Keep turning hands backward and forward, keeping time to the music, until at the end, they make "three little turns" (one hand revolving around the other), and fly away.

Pantomime with the fingers   Translation by Elaine Birnie Mead   Words and tune traditional (French)

Ain - si font, font, font, Les pe - ti - tes marion - ettes, Ain - si
See them dance, so! so! All the lit - tle marion - ettes, See them

font, font, font, Trois p'tits tours et puis s'en vont!
dance, so! so! Three lit - tle turns, and off they go!

55

ROCKABYE, BABY

Words and tune traditional

Harmonized by Katharine Tyler Wessells

Rock - a - bye, ba - by, on the tree - top.

When the wind blows, the cra - dle will rock; When the bough breaks, the

cra - dle will fall, And down will come ba - by, cra - dle and all.

AU CLAIR DE LA LUNE

French words traditional   Translated and harmonized by Katharine Tyler Wessells   Melody attributed to Lully (1633-1687)

57

BYE, BABY BUNTING

Words from Mother Goose   Harmonized by Katharine Tyler Wessells   Tune traditional

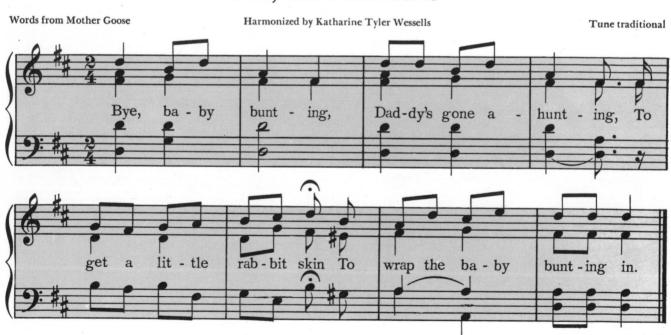

Bye, ba - by bunt - ing, Dad-dy's gone a - hunt - ing, To get a lit - tle rab - bit skin To wrap the ba - by bunt - ing in.

POLLY PUT THE KETTLE ON

Words from Mother Goose · Harmonized by Katharine Tyler Wessells · Tune traditional (English)

Pol-ly put the ket-tle on, Pol-ly put the ket-tle on, Pol-ly put the ket-tle on, We'll all have tea! Su-key, take it off a-gain, Su-key, take it off a-gain, Su-key, take it off a-gain, They've all gone a-way.

CRADLE SONG

Words traditional Arranged by Katharine Tyler Wessells Music by Johannes Brahms

Lul-la-by and good-night, With ros-es be-dight, __ With lil-ies be-decked Is __ ba-by's wee bed, Lay thee down now and rest, May thy slum-ber be blest, Lay thee down now and rest, May thy slum-ber be blest.

JESUS LOVES ME

Words by Anna B. Warner Harmonized by Katharine Tyler Wessells Music by William B. Bradbury

Je-sus loves me, this I know, For the Bi-ble tells me so; Lit-tle ones to Him be-long, They are weak but He is strong. Yes, Je-sus loves me,— Yes, Je-sus loves me,— Yes, Je-sus loves me, The Bi-ble tells me so.

HUSH, MY BABE

Words by Isaac Watts
Harmonized by Katharine Tyler Wessells
Melody by J. J. Rousseau

Hush, my_ babe, lie still and slum - ber. Ho - ly_ an - gels
guard thy_ bed, Heav'n - ly_ bless - ings with - out num - ber
Gent - ly_ fall - ing on_ thy_ head. How much bet - ter
thou art at - tend - ed, than the_ Son of God could be, __

When from Heav-en He de - scended, And be - came a child like thee.

JESUS, TENDER SHEPHERD

Words by Mary Duncan

Music by Mrs. Charles Barnard

Je - sus, ten - der Shep-herd, hear me; Bless Thy lit - tle lamb to-night;

Thro' the dark-ness be Thou near me: Keep me safe till morn-ing light.

JINGLE BELLS

Words traditional   Arranged by Katharine Tyler Wessells   Tune by J. Pierpont

Dashing through the snow, in a one-horse o-pen sleigh, And o'er the fields we go, Laughing all the way. The bells on bob-tail ring, Mak-ing spir-its bright. What fun it is to ride and sing A sleighing song to-night.

CHORUS

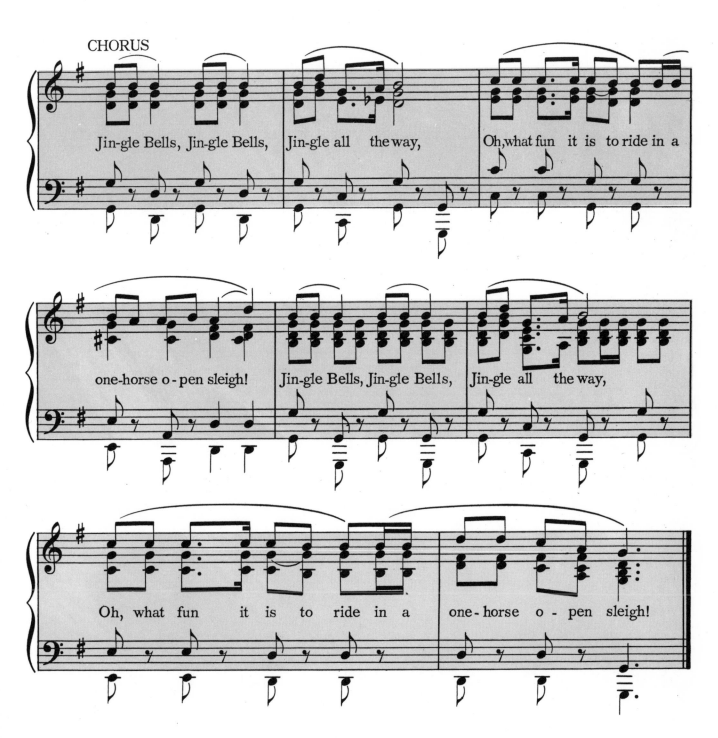

Jin-gle Bells, Jin-gle Bells, Jin-gle all the way, Oh, what fun it is to ride in a

one-horse o-pen sleigh! Jin-gle Bells, Jin-gle Bells, Jin-gle all the way,

Oh, what fun it is to ride in a one-horse o-pen sleigh!

THREE BLIND MICE

Words from Mother Goose   Harmonized by Katharine Tyler Wessells   Tune traditional

Three blind mice, — Three blind mice, — See how they

run! — See how they run! — They all ran af-ter the

farm-er's wife, Who cut off their tails with a carv-ing knife. Did you

ev-er see such a sight in your life As three blind mice?

THE STAR-SPANGLED BANNER

Words by Francis Scott Key   Arranged by Katharine Tyler Wessells   Music by John Stafford Smith

O — say, can you see, by the dawn's ear - ly light, What so proud - ly we hailed, at the twi - light's last gleam-ing? Whose broad stripes and bright stars, through the per - il - ous fight, O'er the ram-parts we watched, were so gal - lant - ly streaming? And the rock-et's red glare, the bombs